First published in the UK in 2022 by Studio Press,
an imprint of Bonnier Books UK,
4th Floor, Victoria House, Bloomsbury Square, London. WC1B 4DA
Owned by Bonnier Books,
Sveavägen 56, Stockholm, Sweden

bonnierbooks.co.uk

© 2022 MARVEL

MIX
Paper from
responsible sources
FSC® C018236

Printed in Poland
1 3 5 7 9 10 8 6 4 2

ISBN 978-1-80078-402-4

11

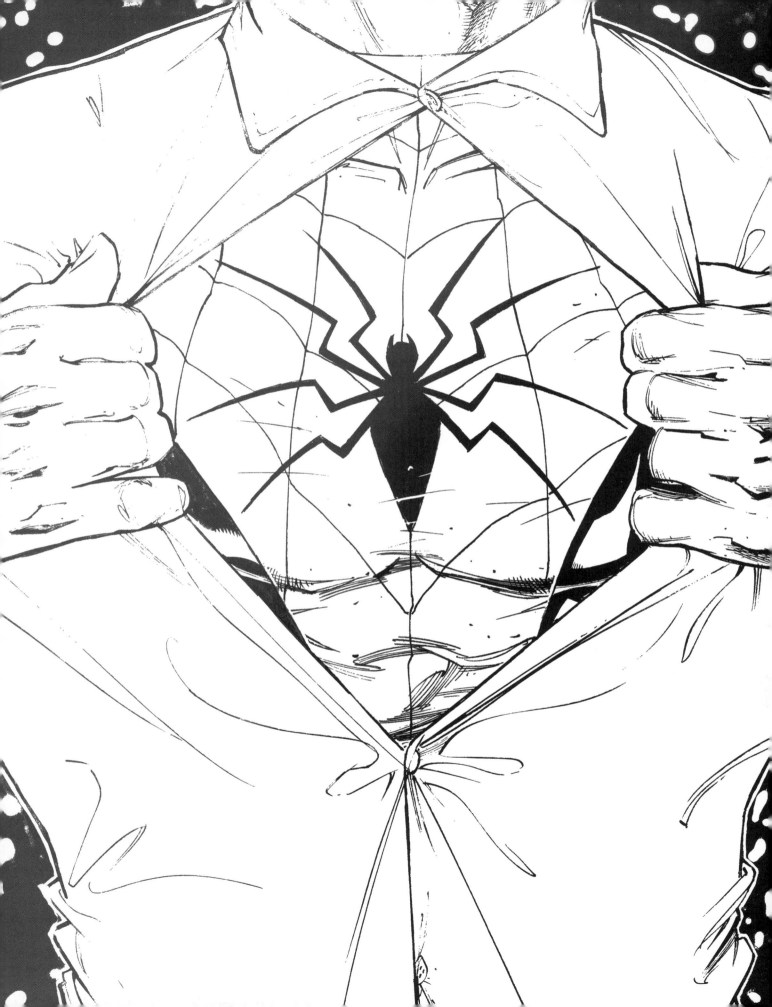

-- CAPTAIN
UNIVERSE ???

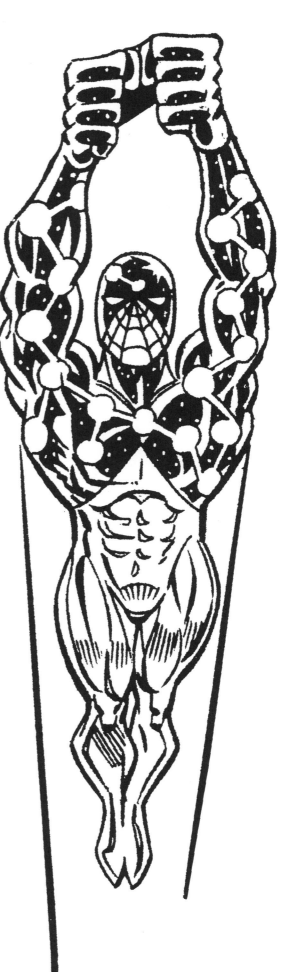

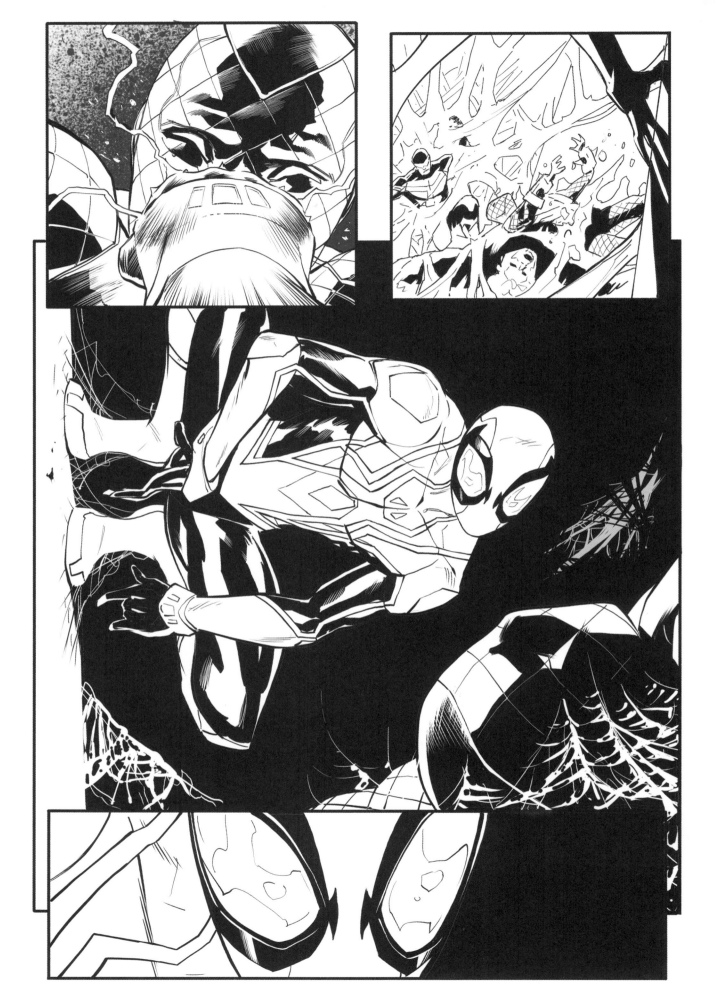

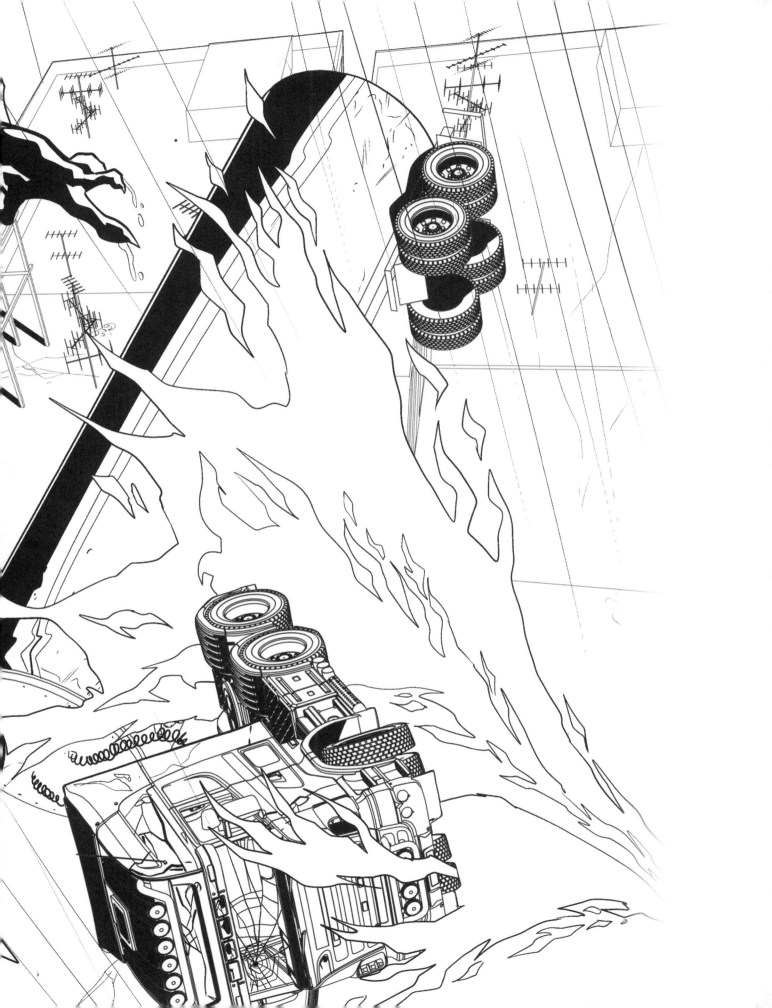

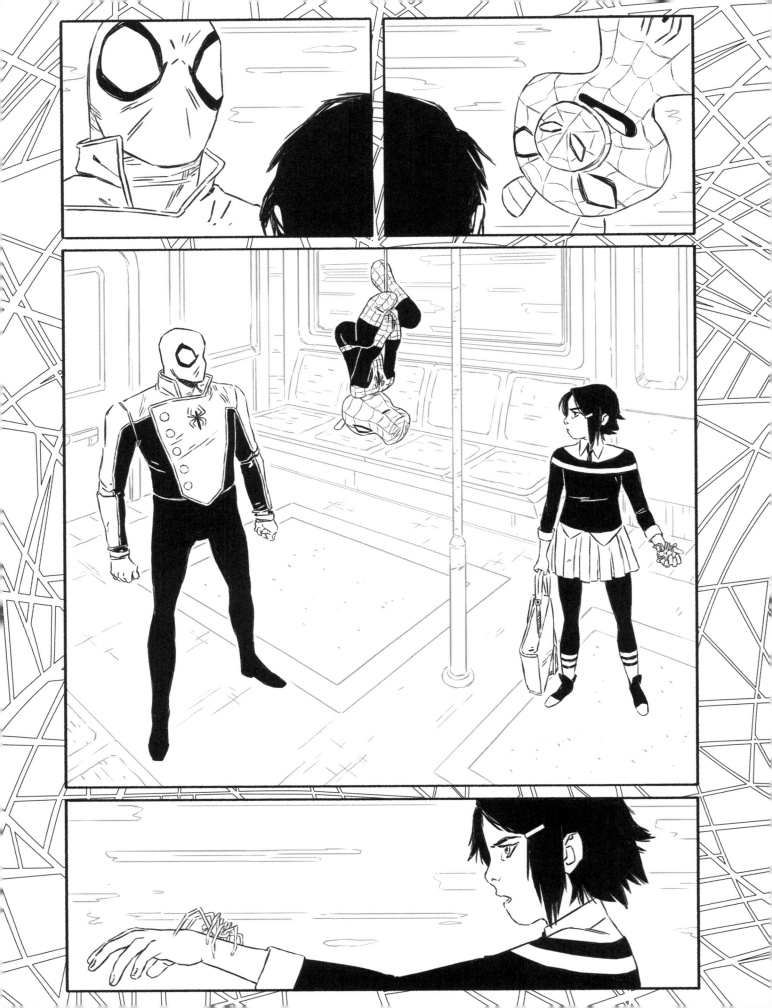

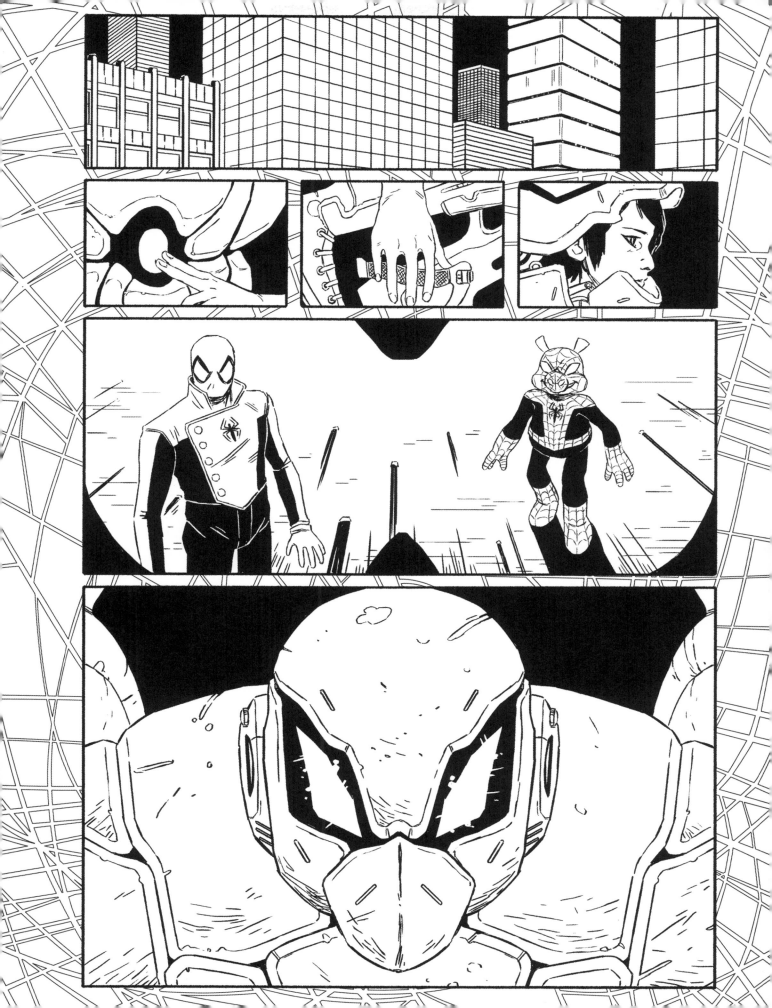

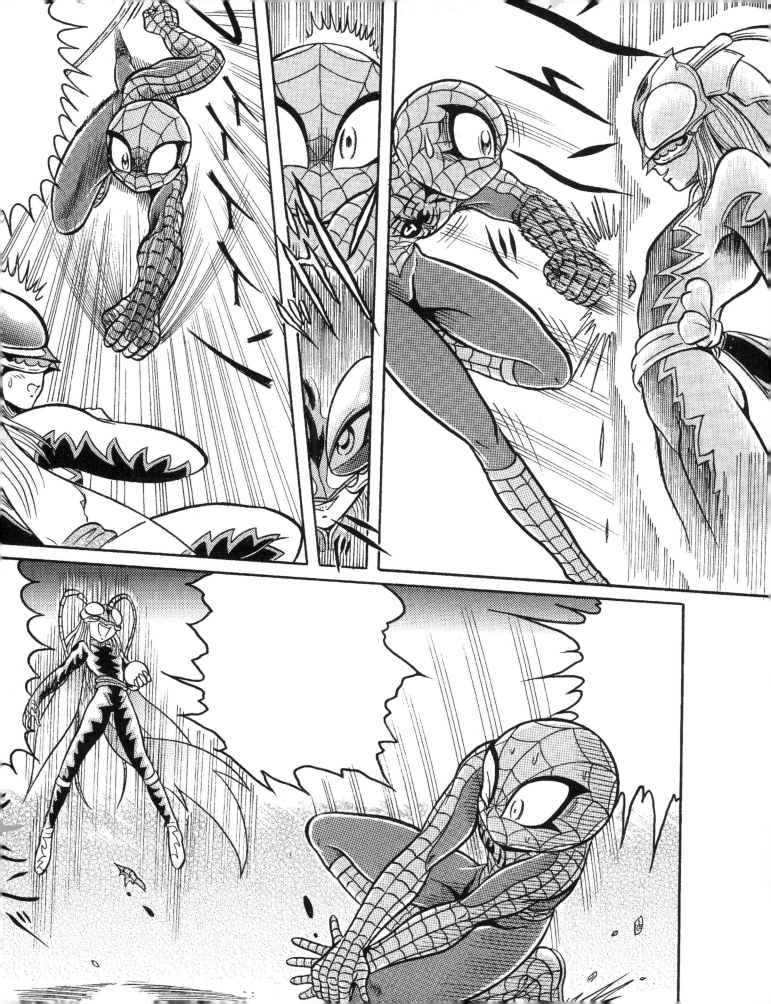

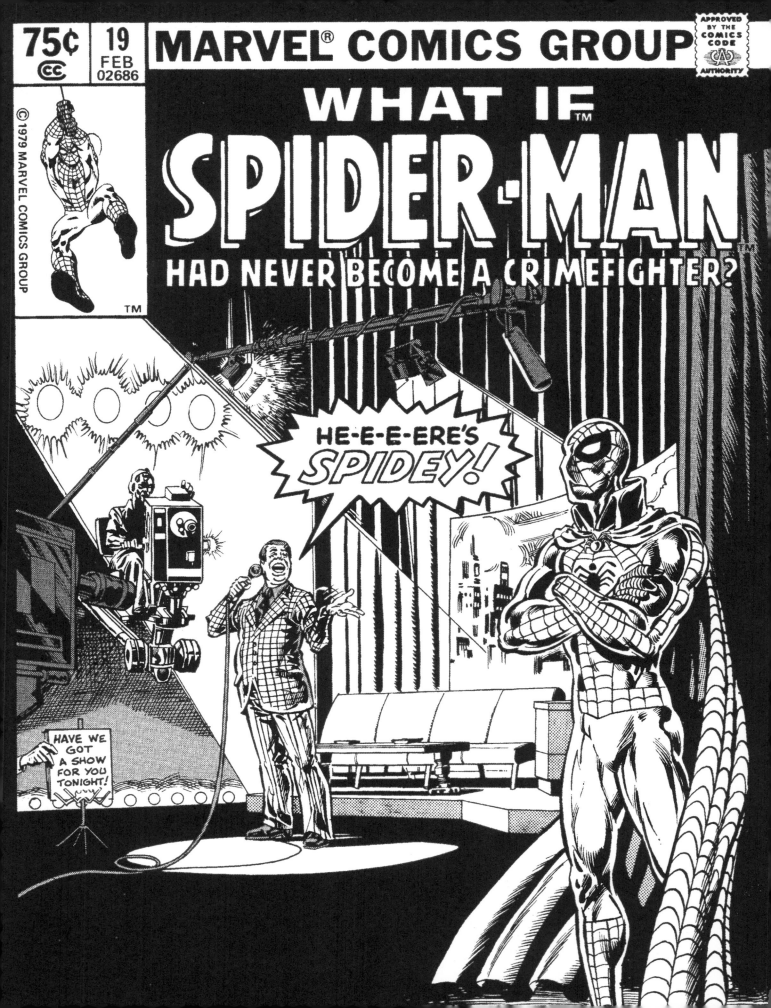